TOTALLY AMAZING MAZES

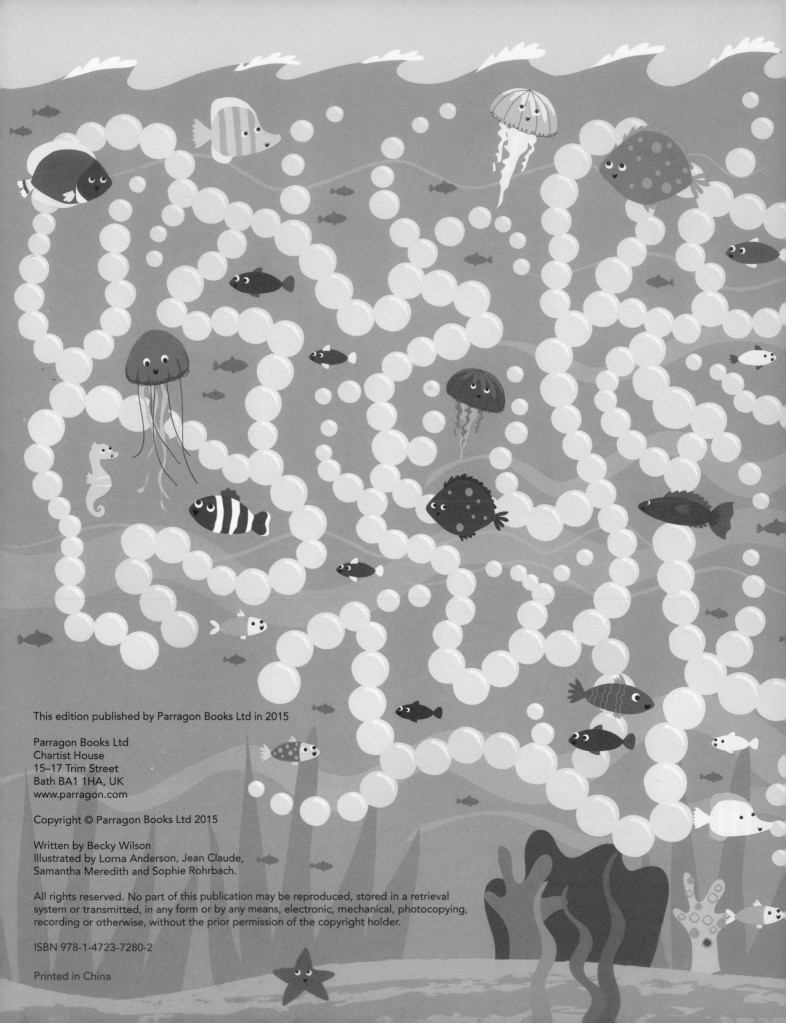

This edition published by Parragon Books Ltd in 2015

Parragon Books Ltd
Chartist House
15–17 Trim Street
Bath BA1 1HA, UK
www.parragon.com

Written by Becky Wilson
Illustrated by Lorna Anderson, Jean Claude,
Samantha Meredith and Sophie Rohrbach.

ISBN 978-1-4723-7280-2

Printed in China

TOTALLY AMAZING MAZES

PaRragon

Bath • New York • Cologne • Melbourne • Delhi
Hong Kong • Shenzhen • Singapore • Amsterdam

Help the zombie hunter find a route to catch all 10 escaped zombies, then return them to the graveyard.

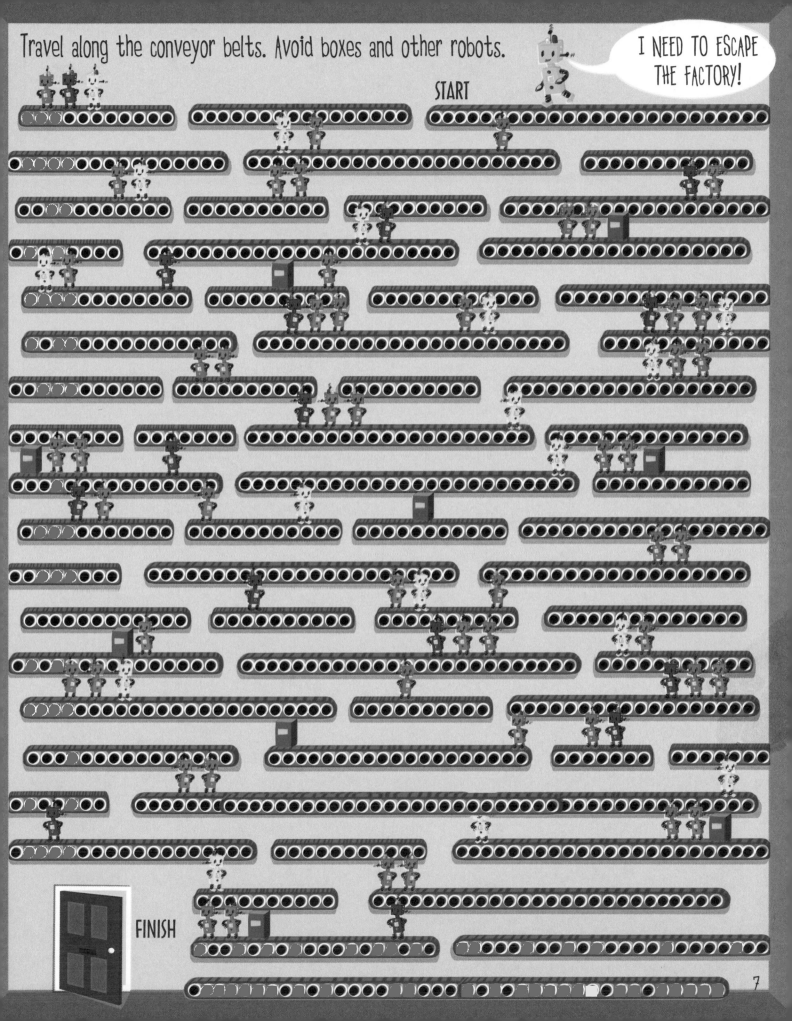

Help Little Fish escape Octopus's tangly arms.

START

FINISH

9

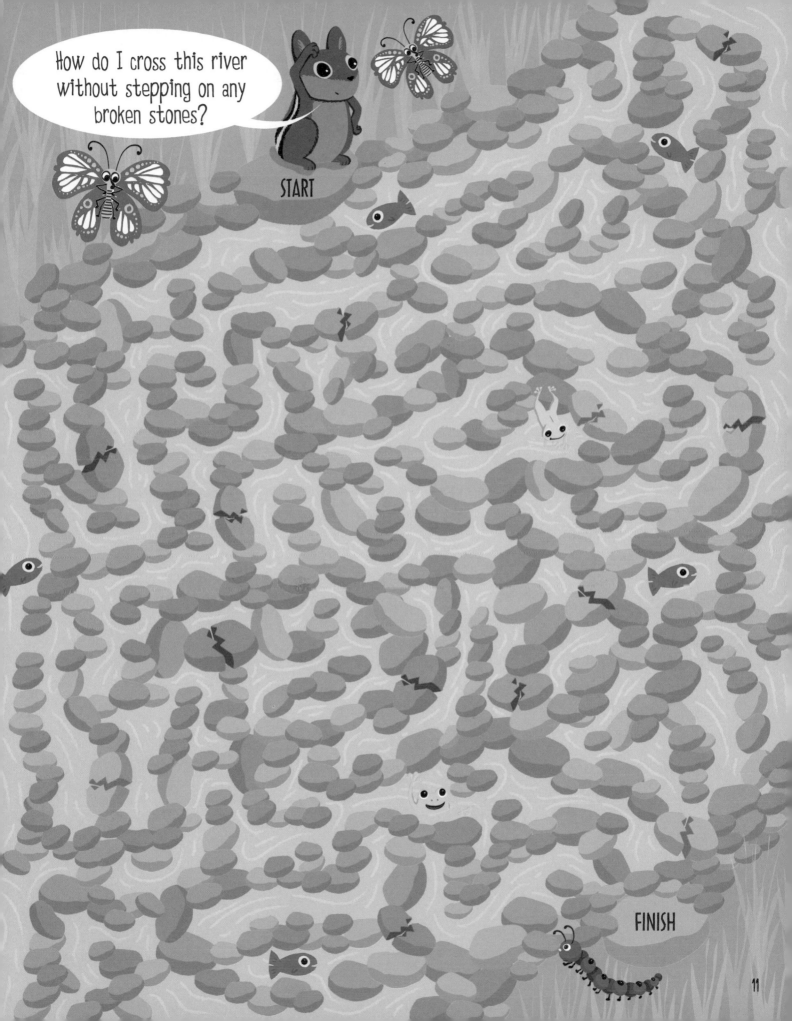

Help Ella find the way between the umbrellas to her matching umbrella.

START

12

FINISH

13

Twelve teachers have been turned into monsters in a science experiment disaster. Collect the bottle of antidote from the science lab...just don't bump into any monsters on the way!

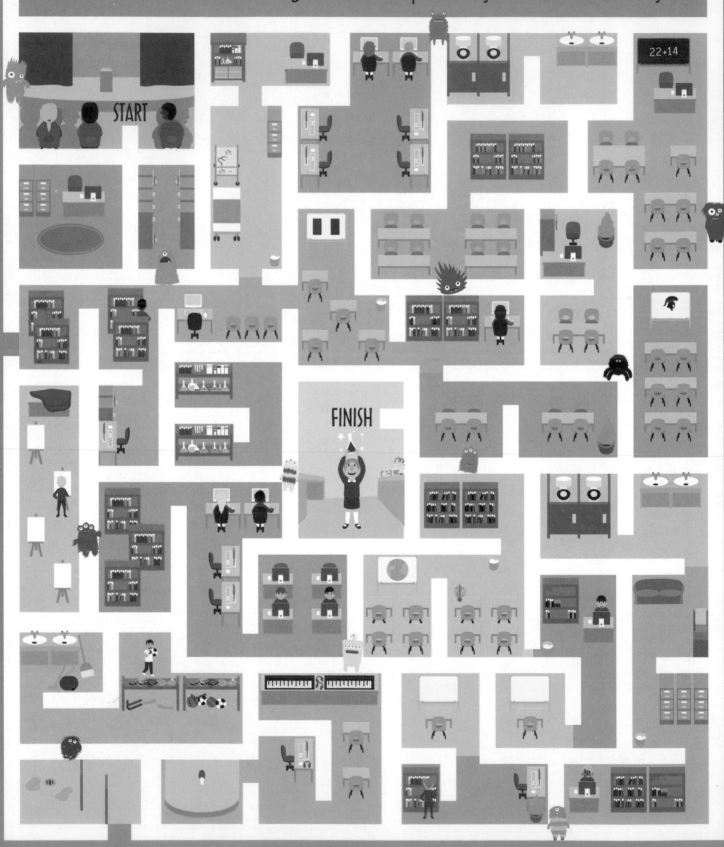

START

FINISH

22+14

FINISH

This car isn't ready to be crushed. Drive it out of the scrapyard.

START

FINISH

19

Meet Stunt Pilot Penguin, about to perform another death-defying trick. Follow the vapour trails to land him safely.

START

START

Way to go,
Stunt Pilot Penguin!

FINISH

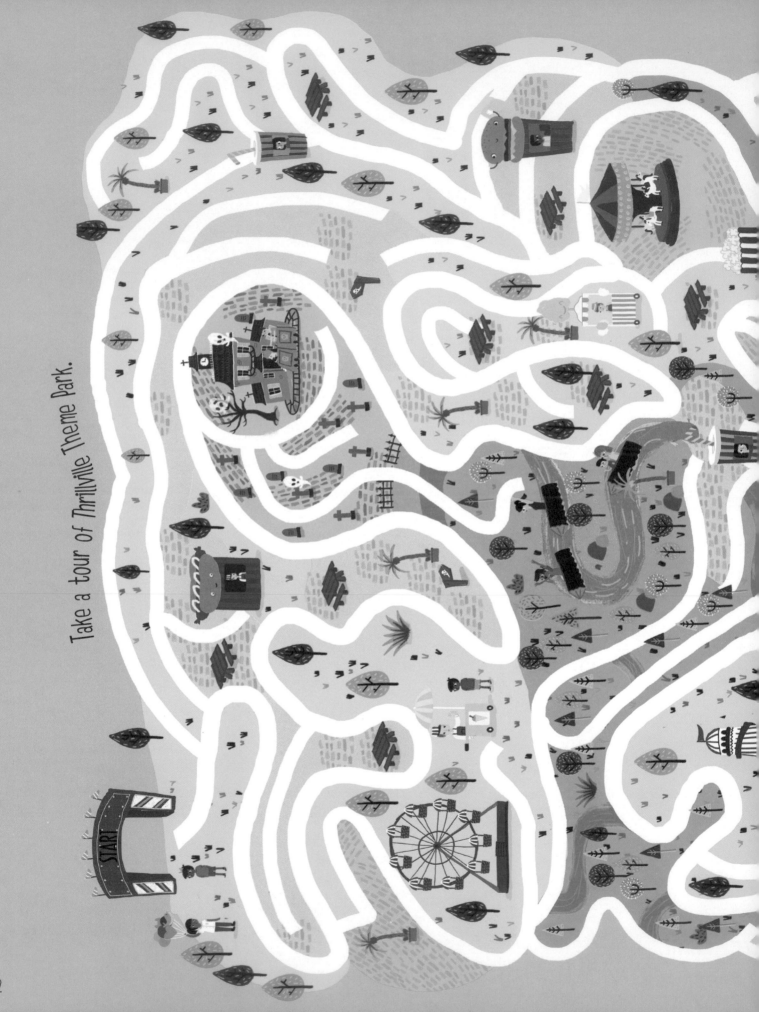

Take a tour of Thrillville Theme Park.

START

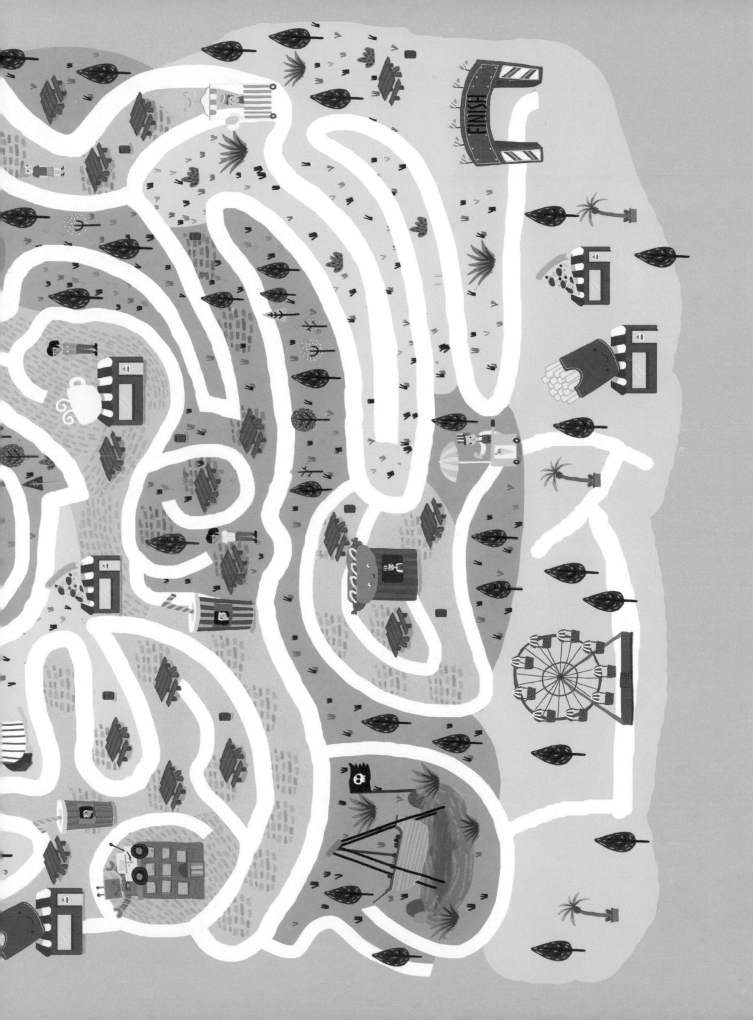

FINISH

23

Help the caterpillar munch its way along
a trail of leaves to its friend.

START

FINISH

24

Use the empty ladders to get Roofer Rob to the leaky roof.

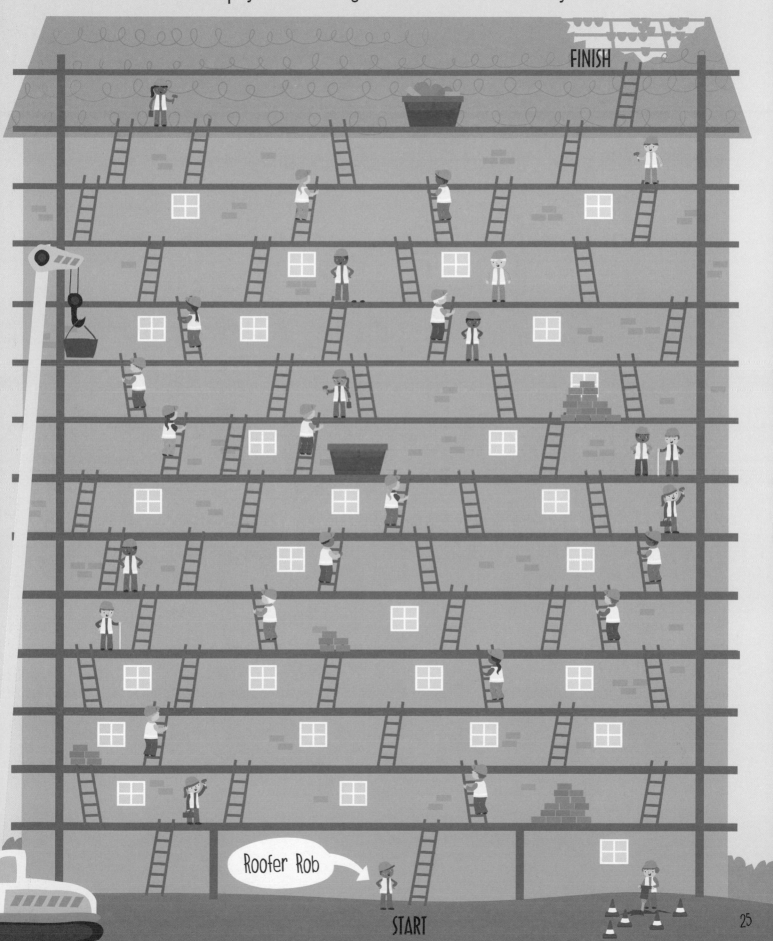

FINISH

Roofer Rob

START

25

Uh-oh! Follow the bubbles to help this scuba diver back to the boat – quick!

SHARK!

START

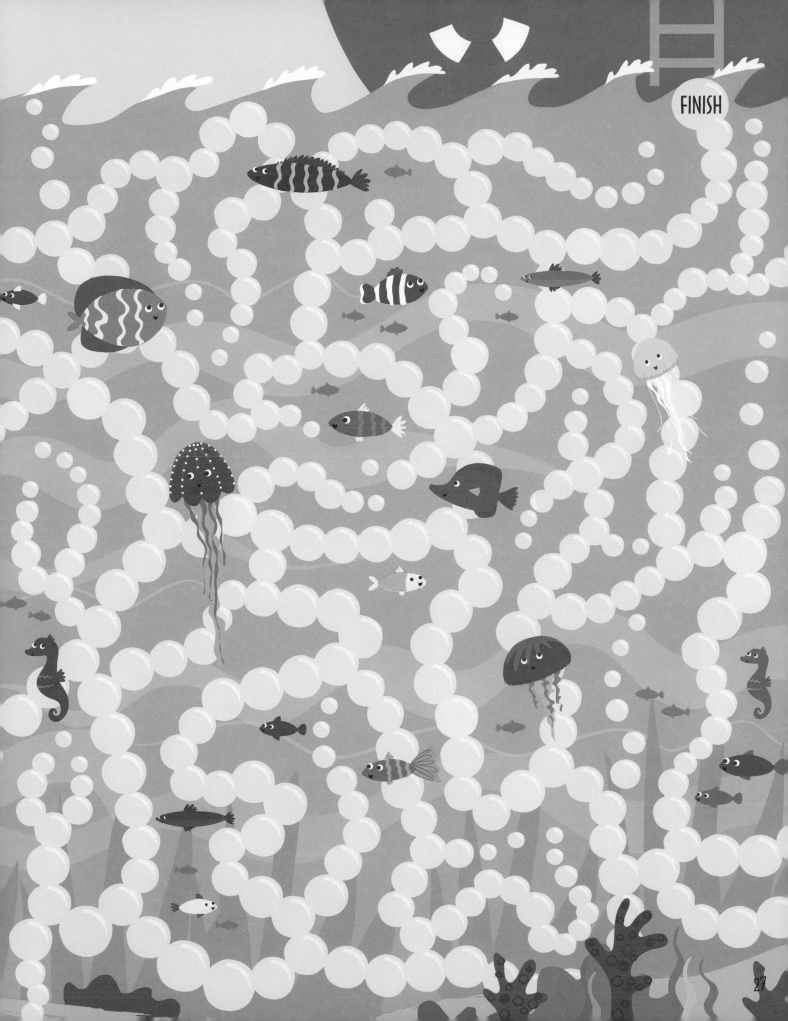

FINISH

27

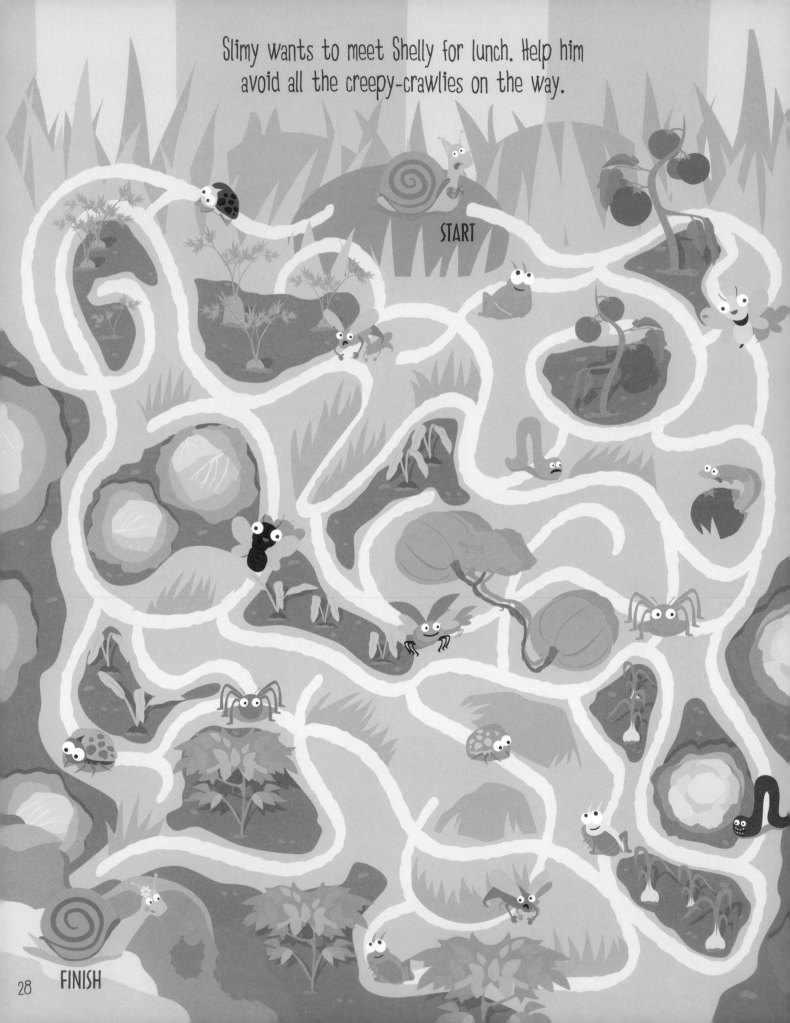

Slimy wants to meet Shelly for lunch. Help him
avoid all the creepy-crawlies on the way.

START

FINISH

Take the escaped mummy back to where it belongs.
Don't scare any tourists on the way!

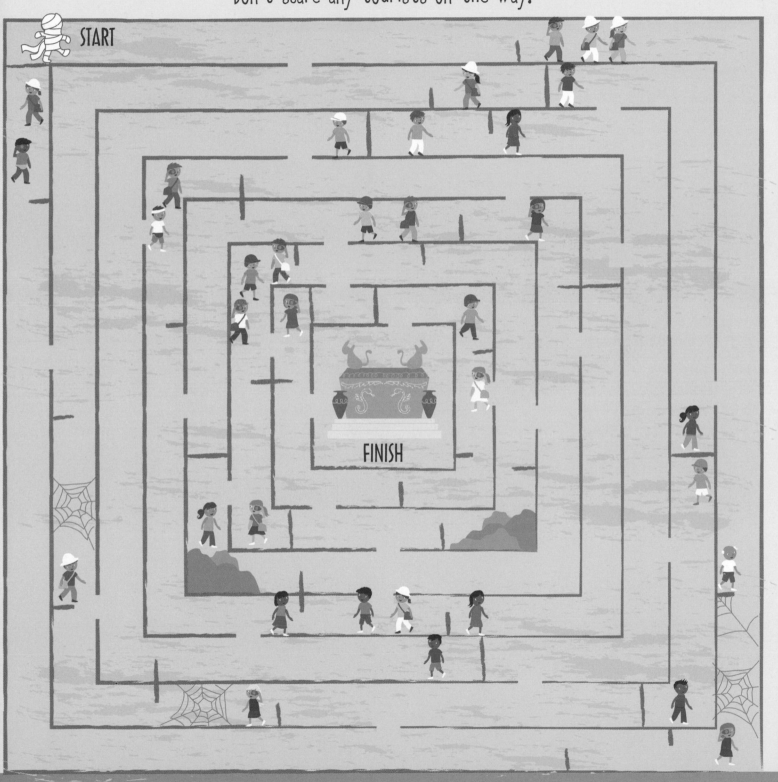

START

FINISH

Avoid the knots in this trainer tangle!

START

FINISH

Quick, you've got a plane to catch! Jump in this taxi to the airport.
Don't go through any red lights along the way.

START

FINISH

Race the mouse to the attic and get through the mouse hole to escape the cat. Use stairs, ladders and open doors to get there.

FINISH

START

35

FINISH

START

WATCH OUT FOR DEADLY RATTLESNAKES!

Carefully climb Cactus Canyon...

36

Deep in the jungle, the explorers are hoping
to catch sight of the rare giant panda.
Travel between the bamboo branches.

START

FINISH

39

Ride the rollercoaster. Just avoid the other cars!

START

FINISH

41

Can you smell toasting marshmallows? Find your way to the campfire.

START

FINISH

Follow the snow trails. There's only one way down!

START

FINISH

FINISH

45

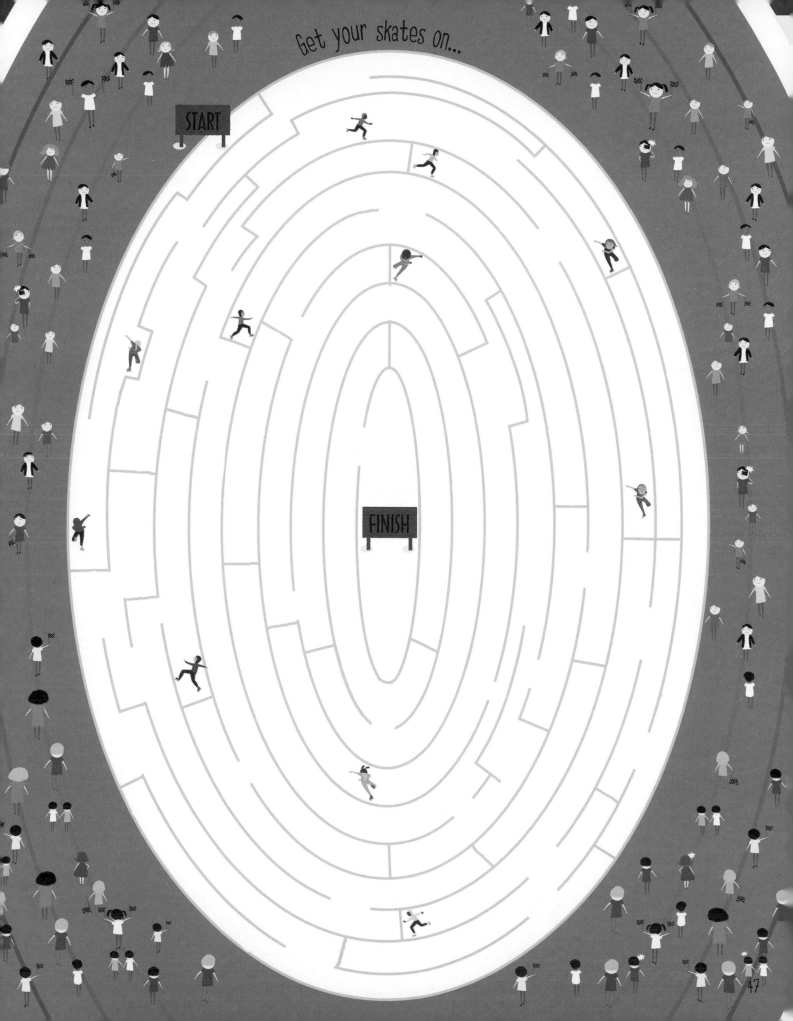

FINISH

START

Unlock the safe to get your hands on the world's largest diamond.

Loop through the lollies for a sweet reward!

START

FINISH

49

Nee-nah! Nee-nah! Drive the fire crew to the rescue!

START

Just don't crash into anything on the way.

HELP!

FINISH

The fire's
this way!

FINISH

START

What's Mr Bear thinking about right now?

FINISH

START

Guide Curtis the cat through the streets to his friends.

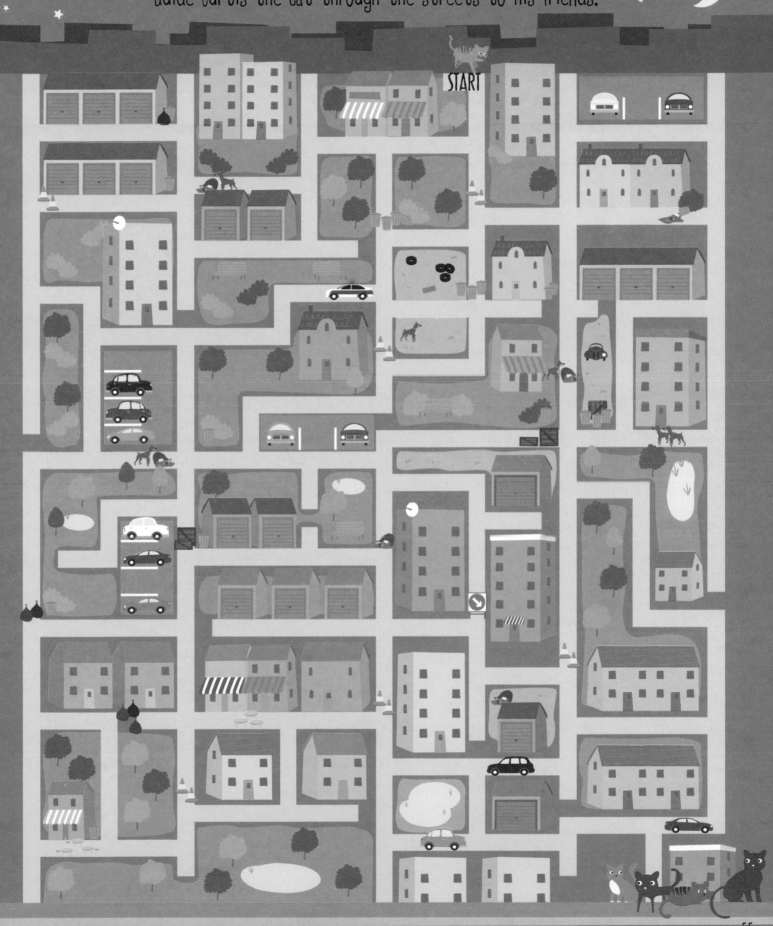

START

FINISH

Princess Polly wants to climb the tower and see the WHOLE kingdom.

The view's great up here!

FINISH

56

START

Guide the seahorse between the seaweed to his true love.

FINISH

REALLY BRAVE

FINISH

TOTALLY AWESOME!

GETTING BRAVER

BEGINNER

START

Take the ski lift to the highest mountain.
You can only travel along cables
without another car on them.

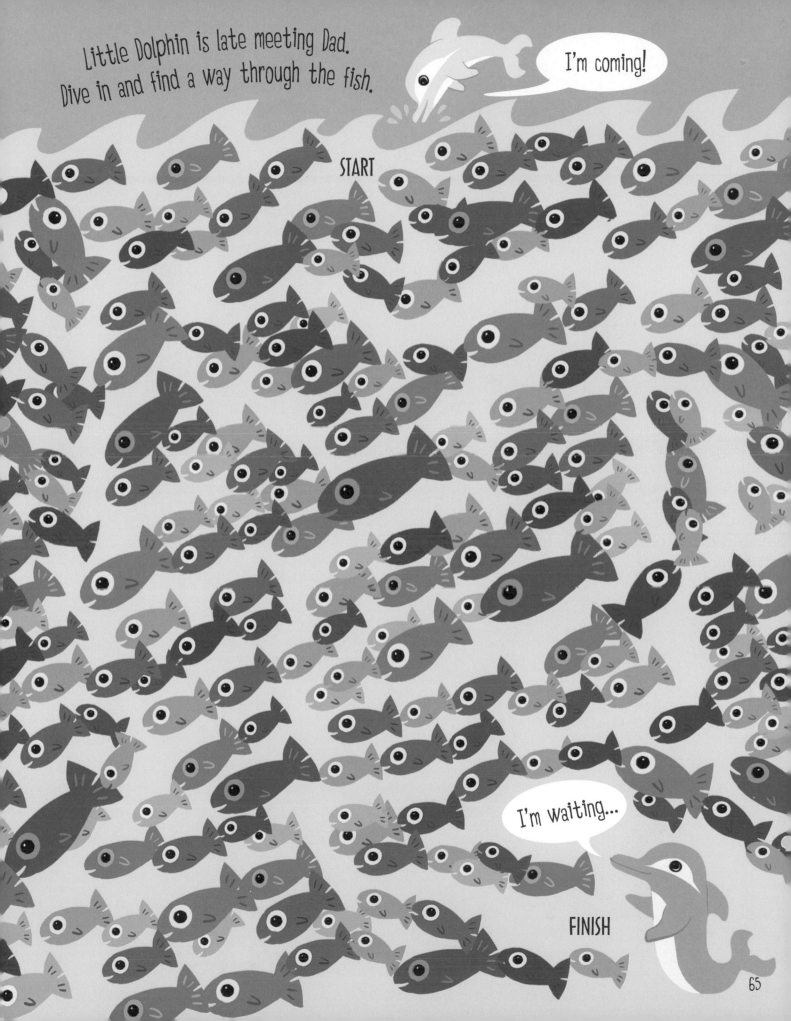

I'm ready for the final piece of the roof...
FINISH
START
I'll bring it right up!

Travel over each blue ghost to zap them all on the way to the end of the level.

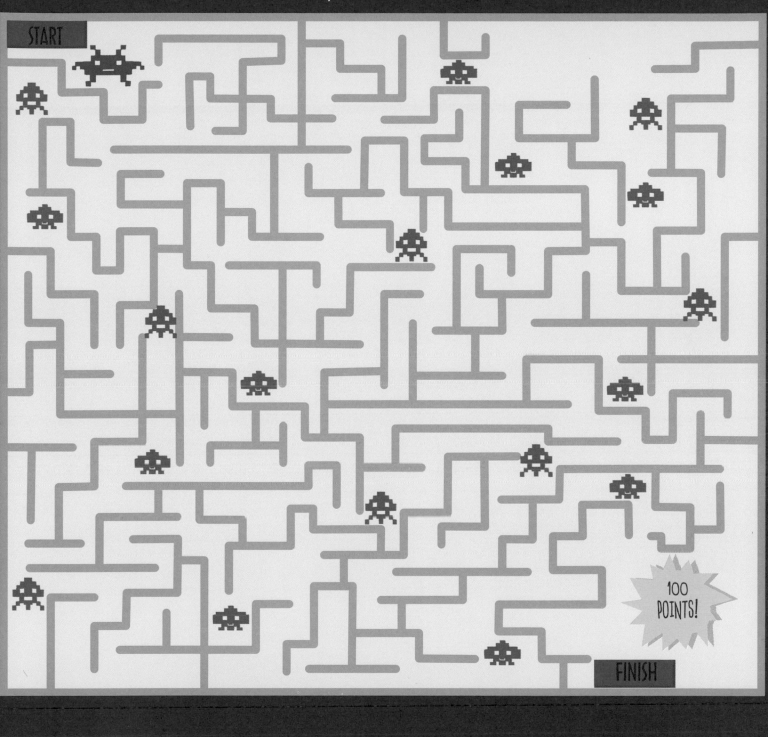

START

FINISH

100 POINTS!

FINISH

START

Baby Bird has taken her first flight, but can't fly back up to the nest. Help her hop back up the branches.

68

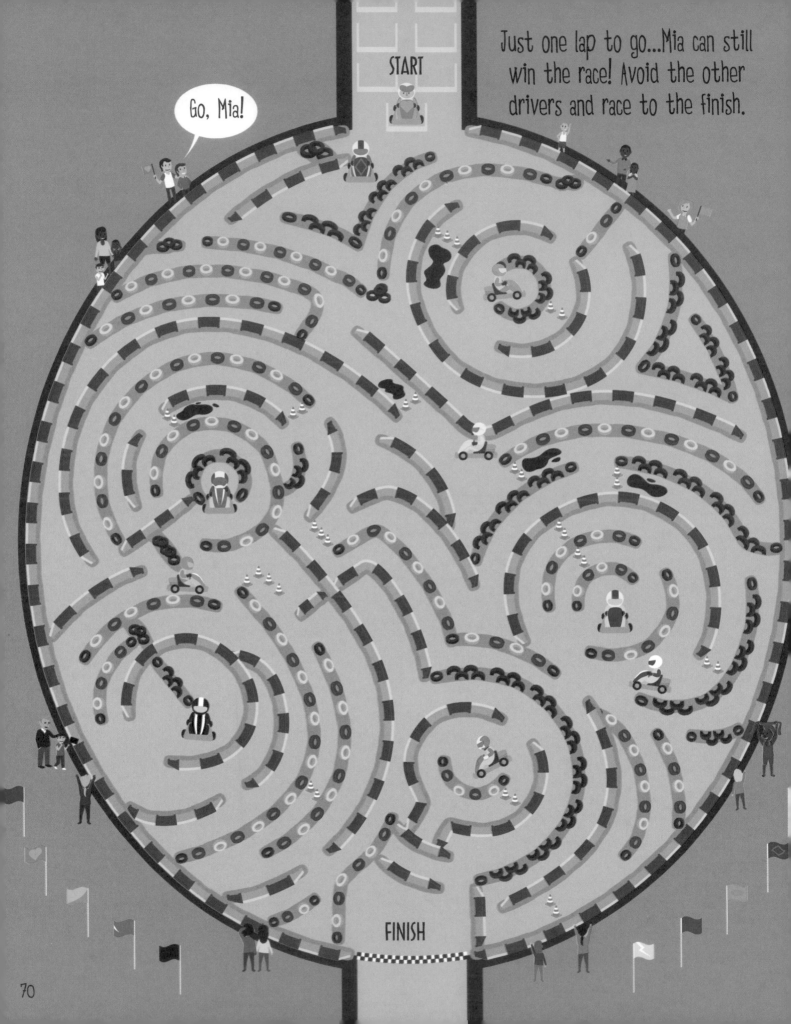

Edge through the hedges to the magical fountain.

START

FINISH

Help Alice follow the tangle of dog leads to the ice cream van to find her pooch!

START

FINISH

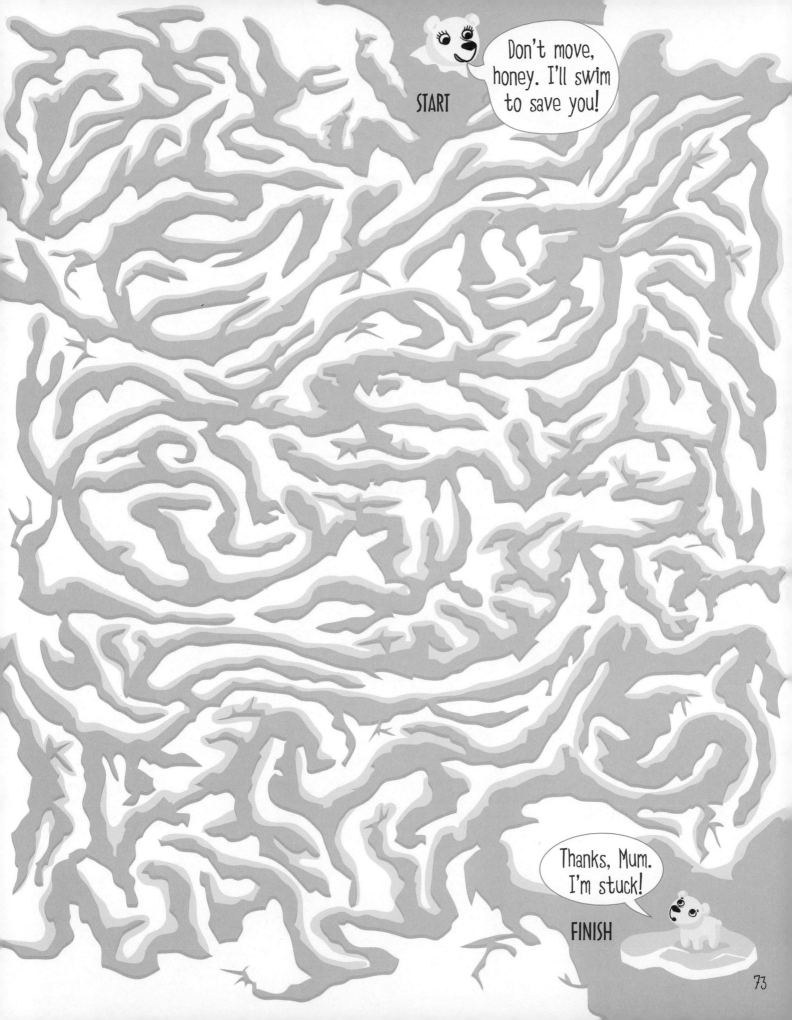

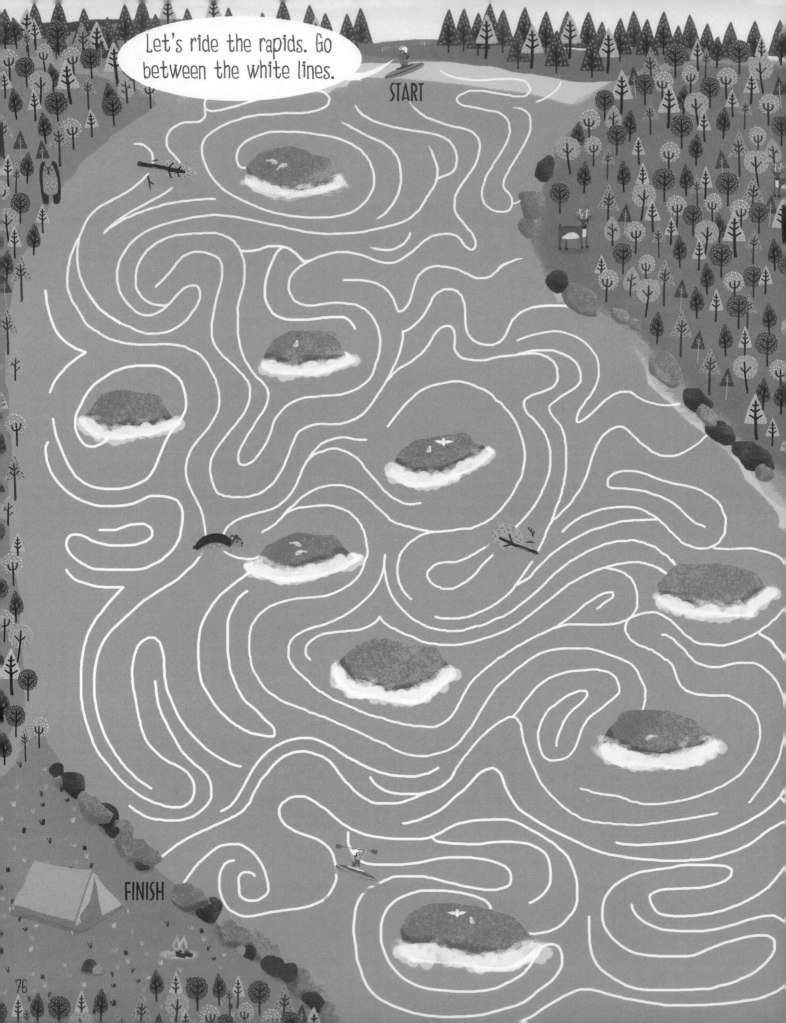

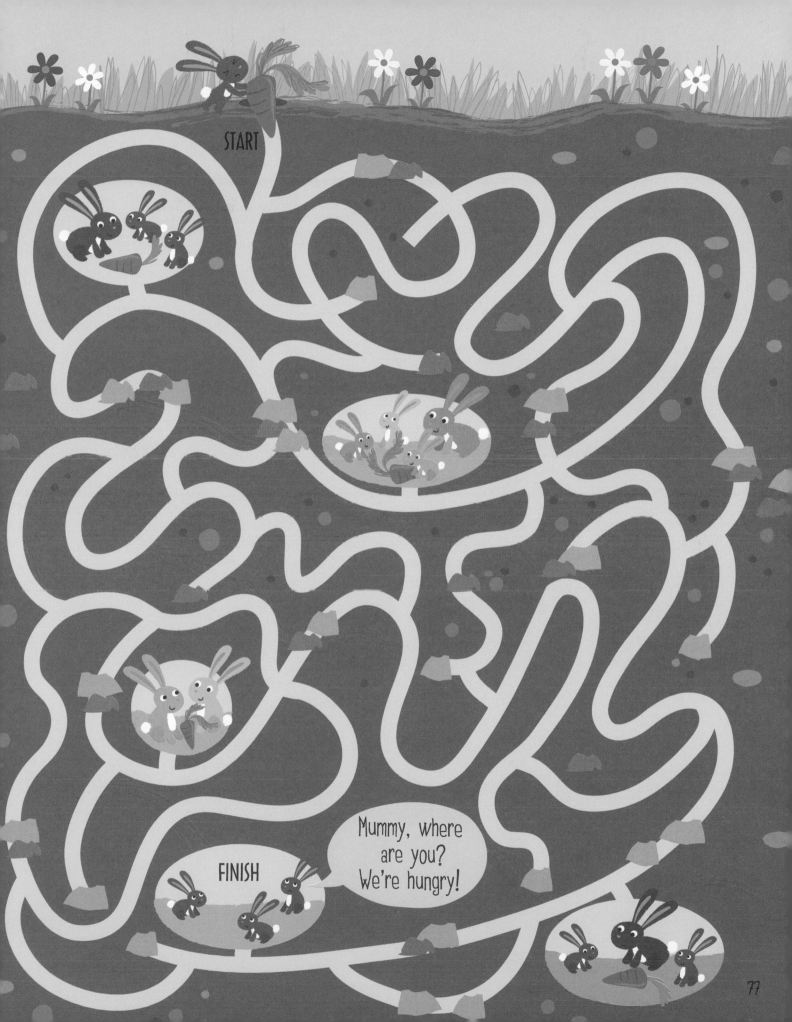

Dodge the craters and get the moon buggy back to the spaceship.

START

WATCH OUT FOR ALIENS!

Seal feeding starts soon. If you're really quick, you can visit the tigers, zebras, shark and raccoons on the way!

SEAL FEEDING AT 2PM

START

FINISH

80

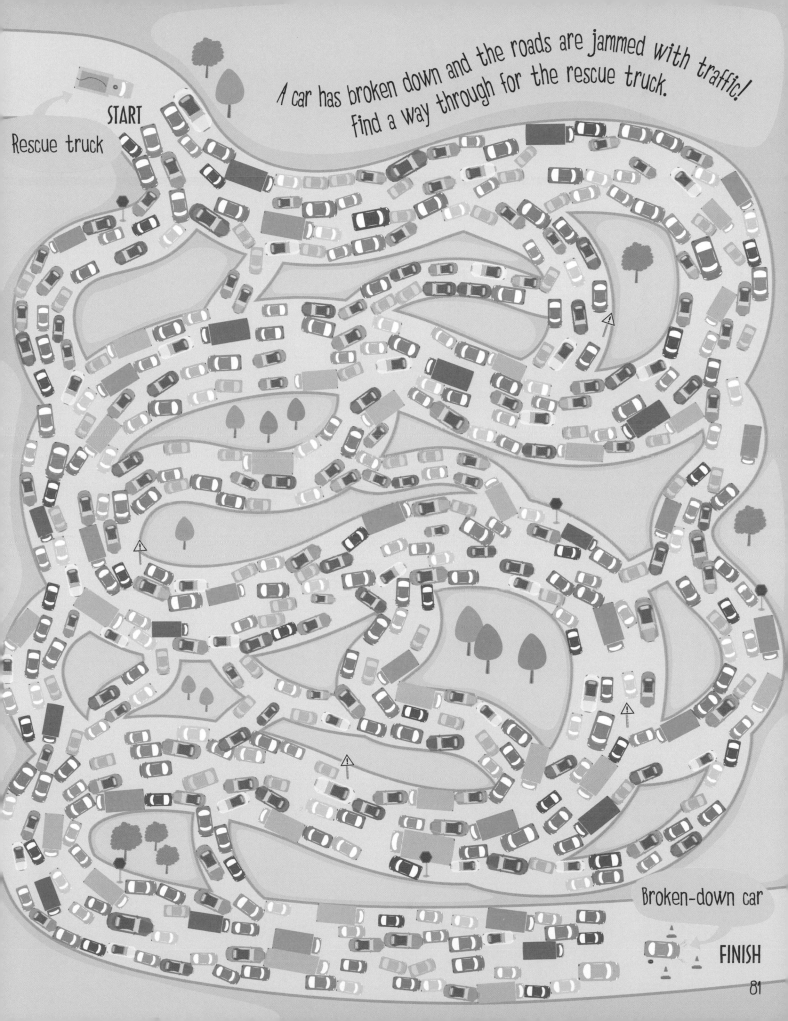

A car has broken down and the roads are jammed with traffic! Find a way through for the rescue truck.

START

Rescue truck

Broken-down car

FINISH

81

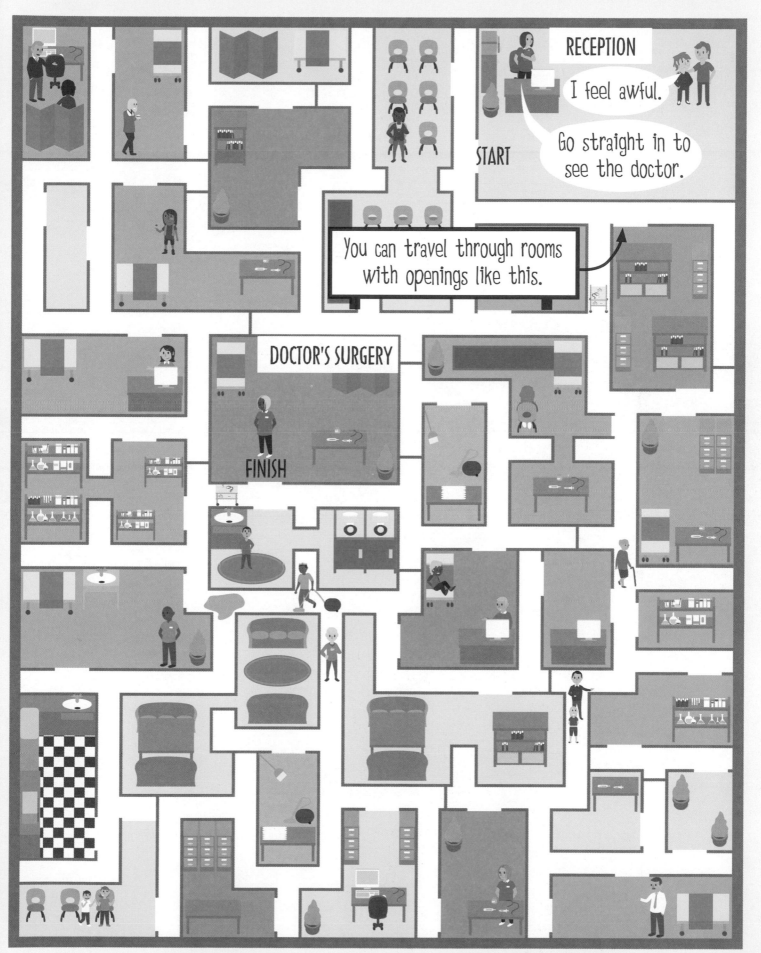

Monkey has lost his troop...

START →

84

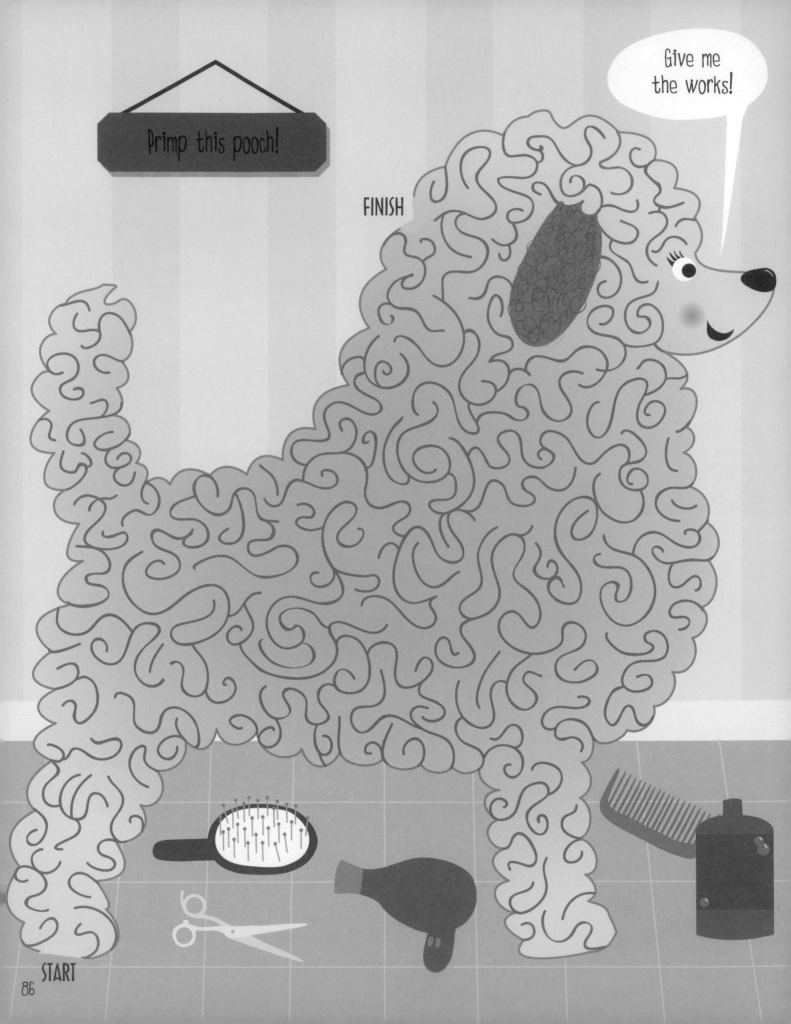

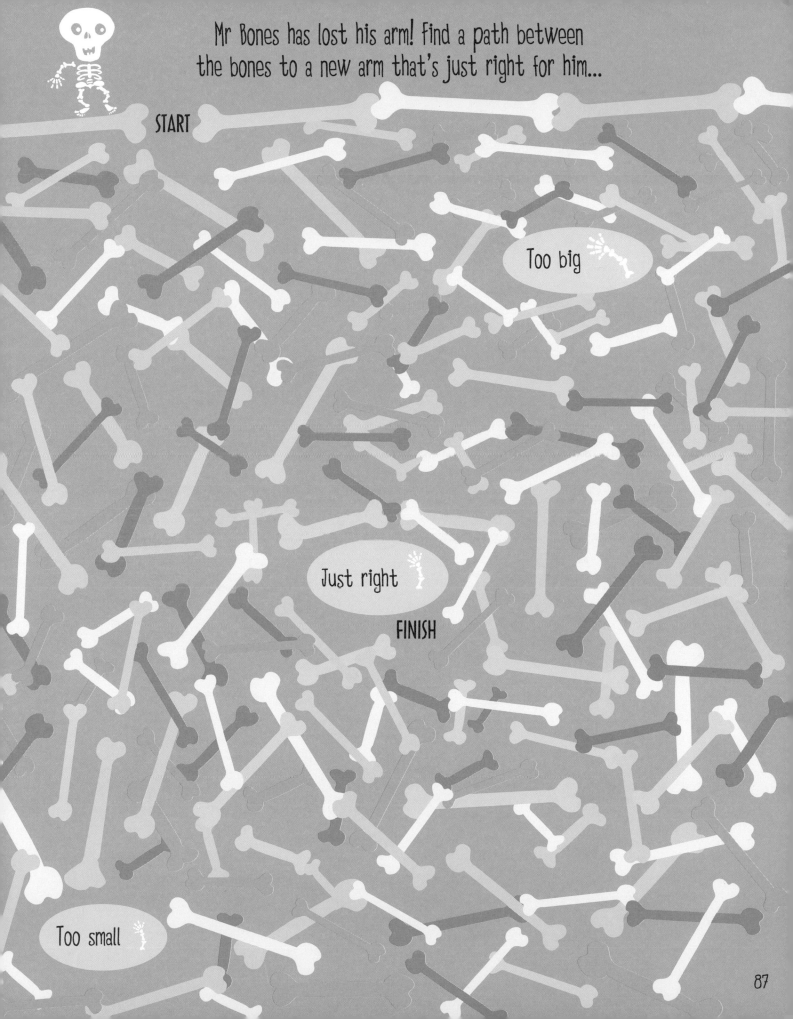

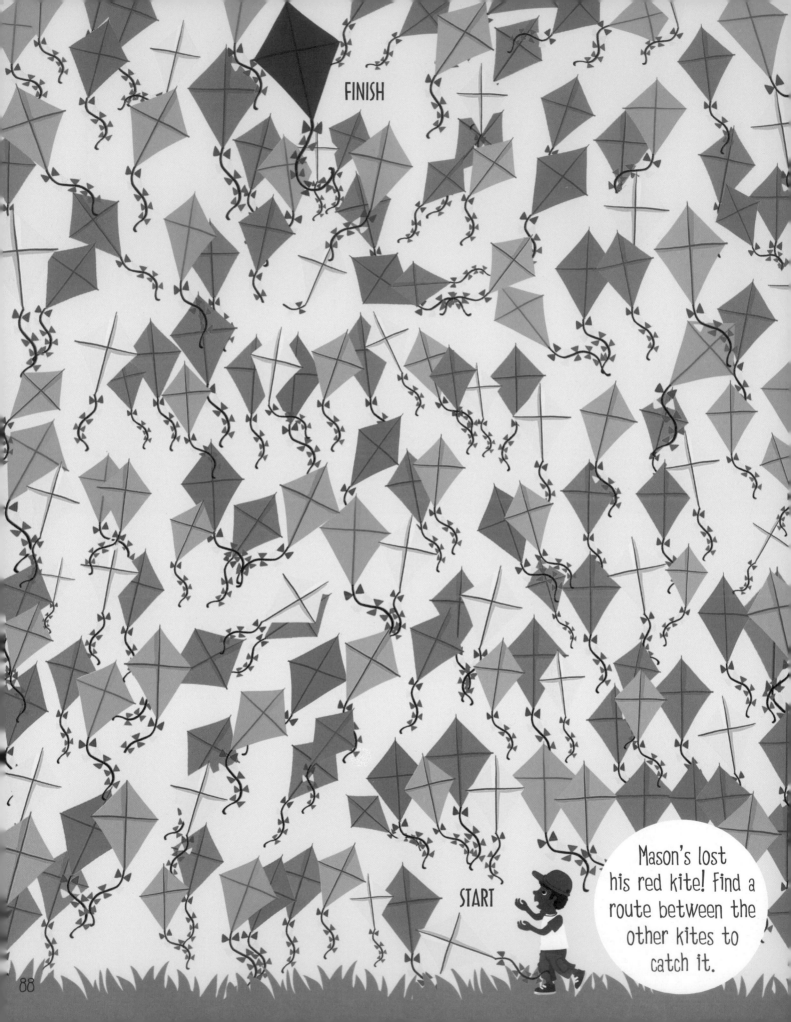

FINISH

START

Mason's lost his red kite! Find a route between the other kites to catch it.

88

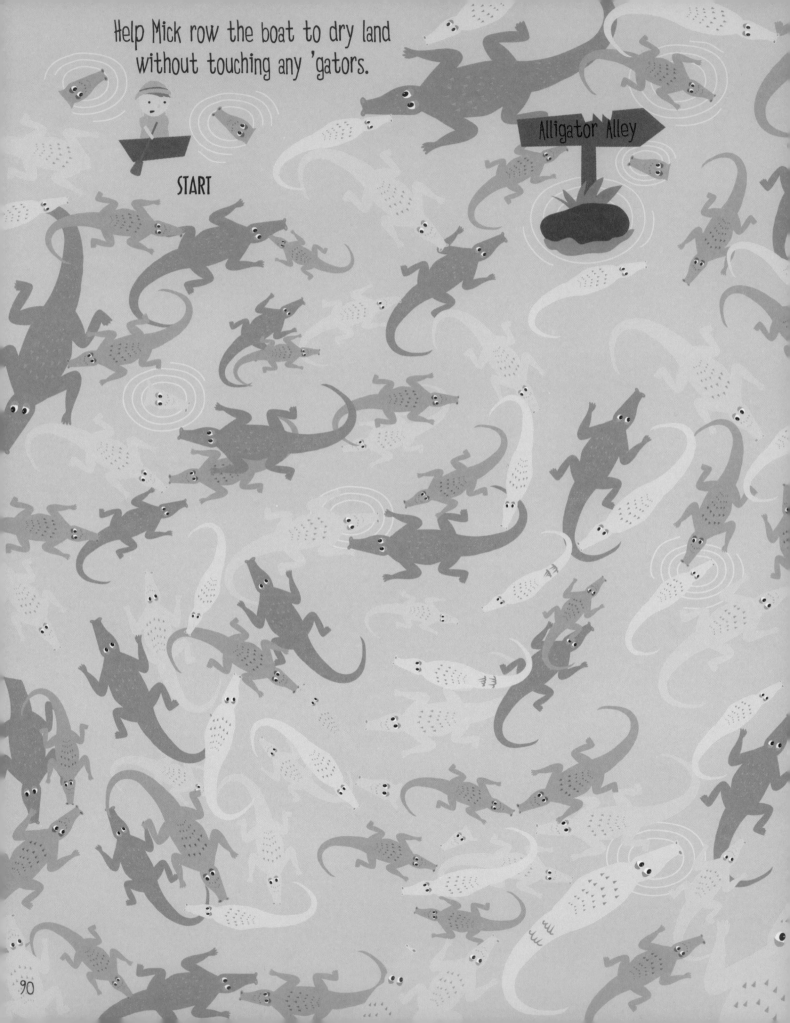

Help Mick row the boat to dry land without touching any 'gators.

START

Alligator Alley

FINISH

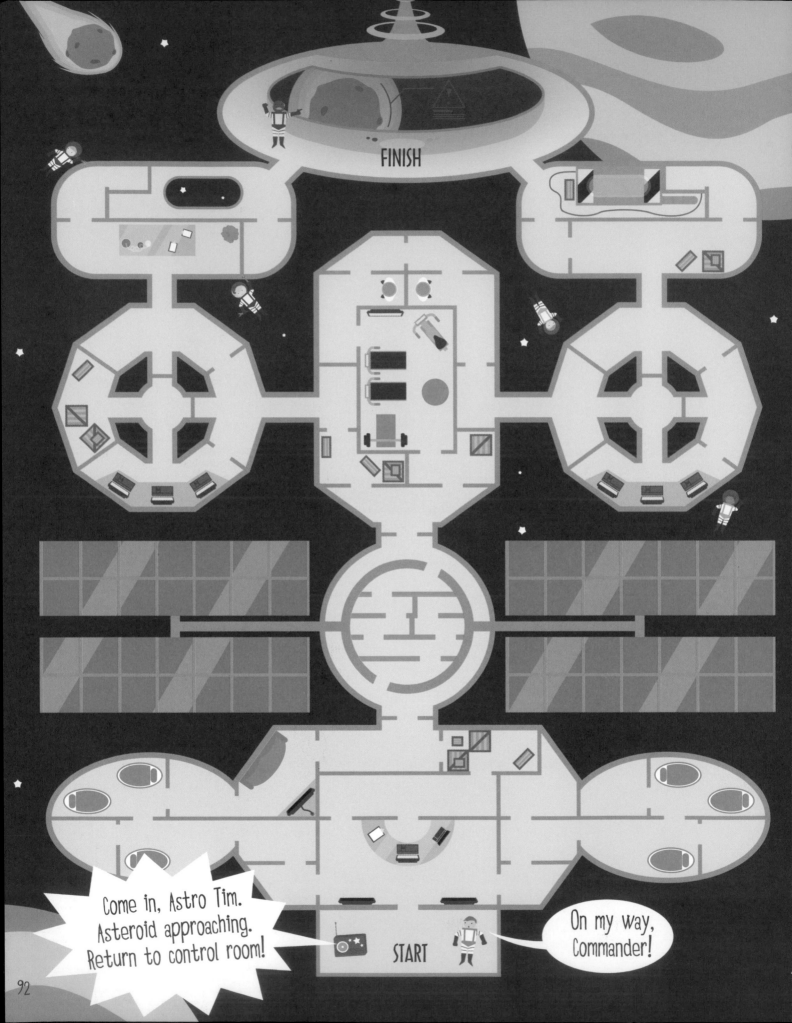

Ellie has lost her daddy in the herd.
Help her find a route between
the other elephants to be
reunited with him.

START

FINISH

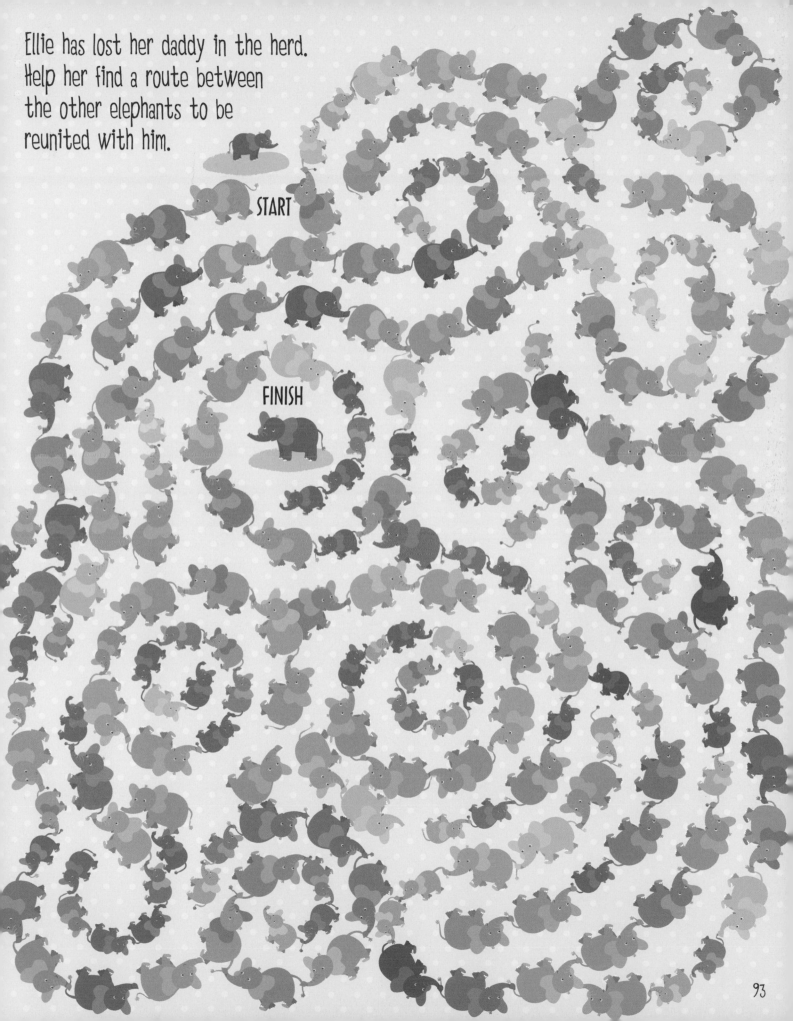

START

Ben's only got ten minutes left in the Adventure Play Park. Pass every red flag to visit each activity and get him to the exit...Mum's waiting!

FINISH

94

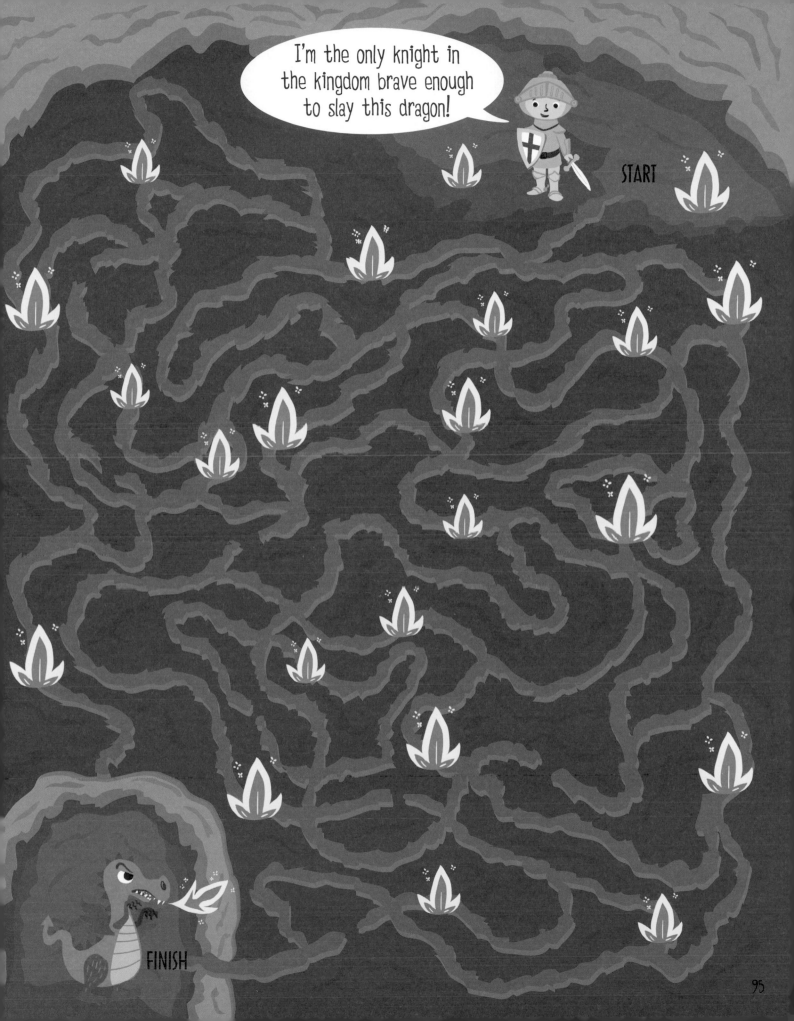

Help One-eyed Violet hop across the pirate ships to reach the treasure.

START

FINISH

96

As long as the bus driver picks up all six children on the way to school, everyone will be on time for class.

START

SCHOOL

FINISH

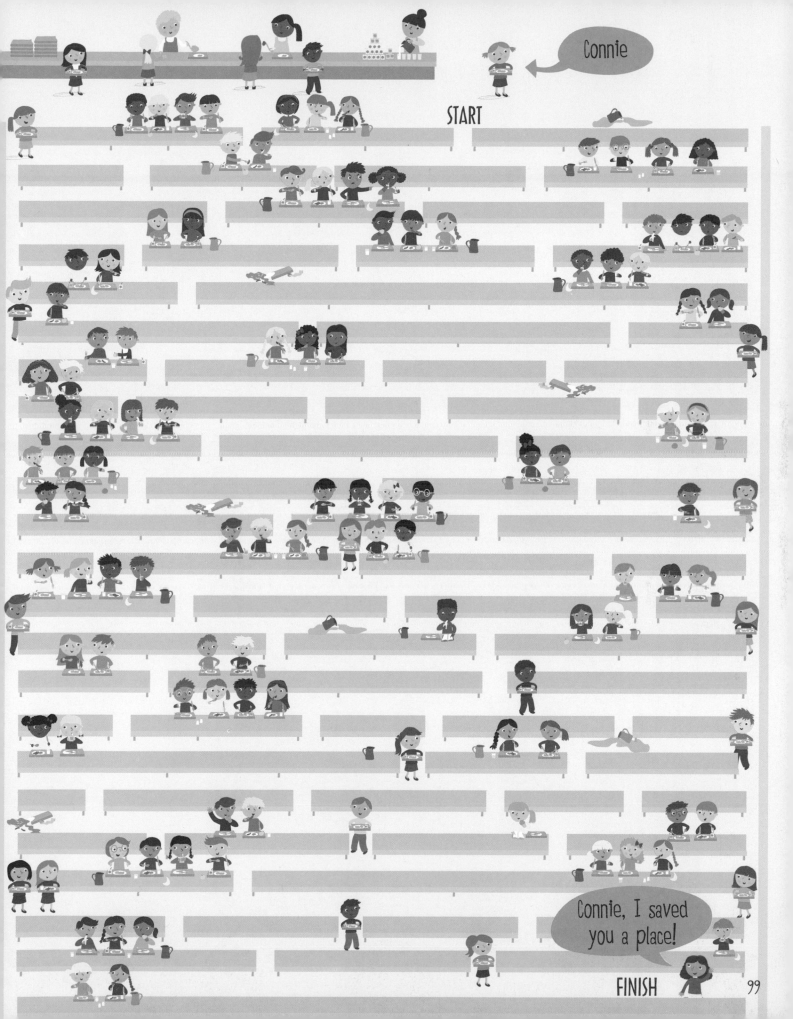

START

Avoid the seaweed tangle
and guide Marissa the mermaid home.

HOME

FINISH

101

It's the rally in the valley!
Skid 'n' slide to the finish line.

START

FINISH

102

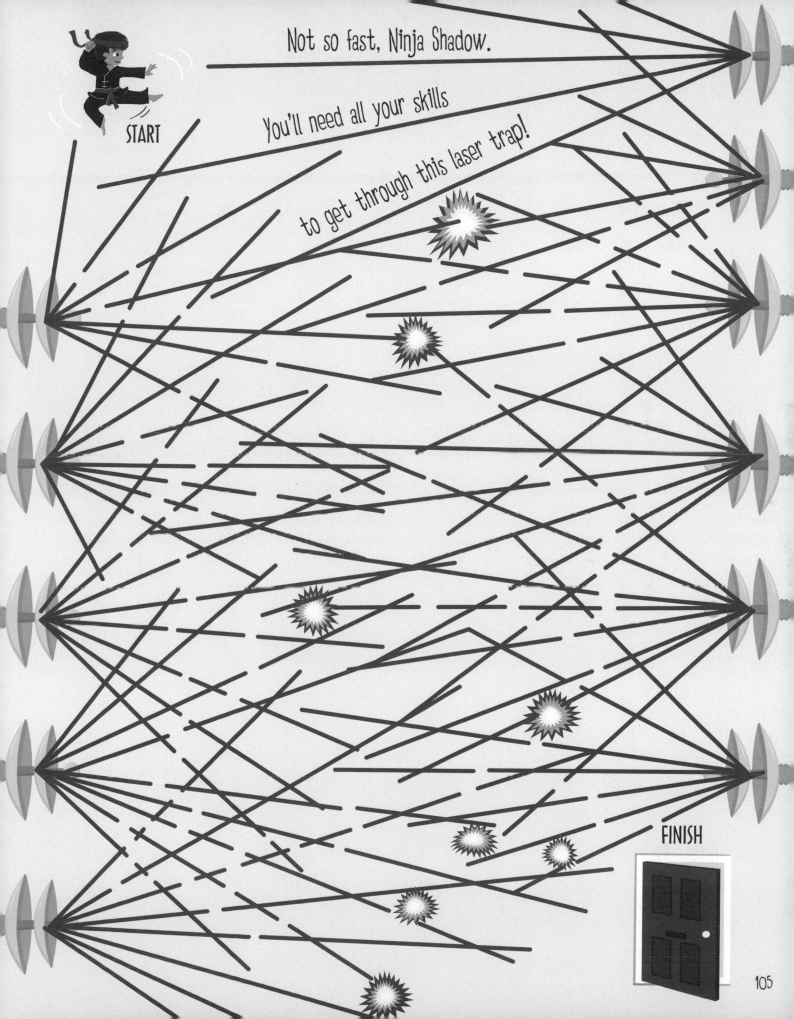

START

Not so fast, Ninja Shadow.

You'll need all your skills

to get through this laser trap!

FINISH

105

Make the most of your safari trip and see every animal along the way!
Watch out for other safari vehicles.

START

106

FINISH

107

There are lots of roadworks and traffic jams today! Can you find a way home?

START

FINISH

108

Mega Blob and his beastly buddies are taking over the city.
There's only one thing for it...RUN!

START

FINISH

110

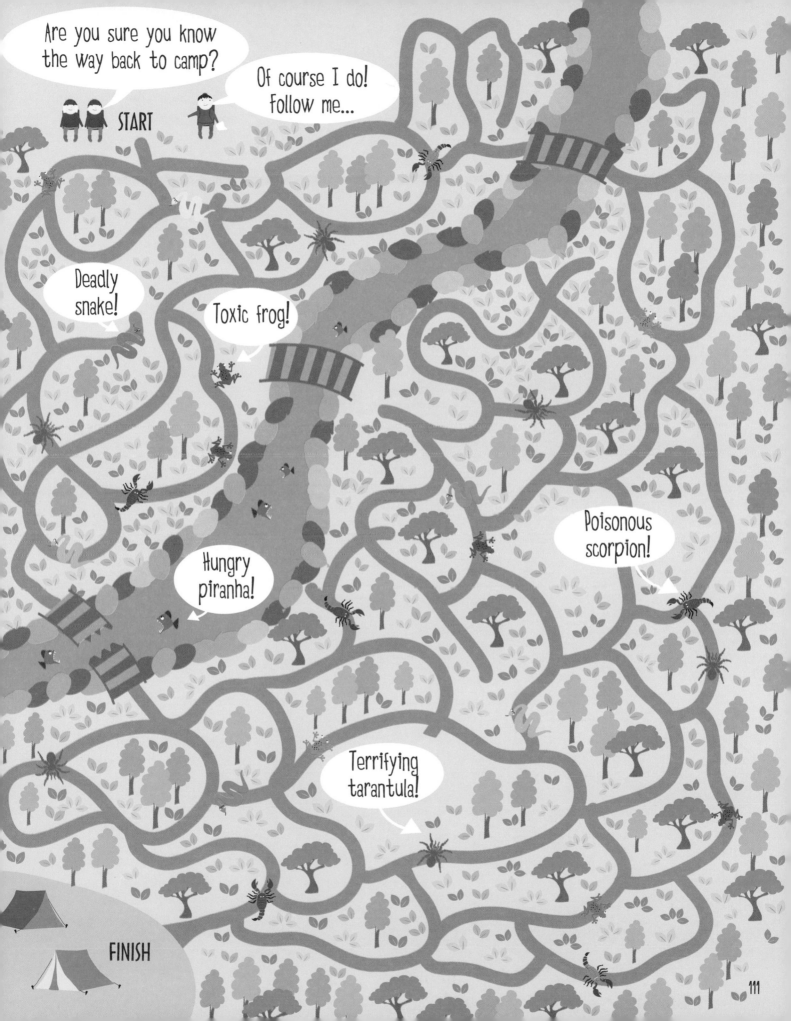

111

FINISH

Help Danny find the rubber in his rucksack.

START

FINISH

Help the woodsman find his log piles.
He's going home to build a toasty fire!

START

FINISH

115

Woof!

FINISH

117

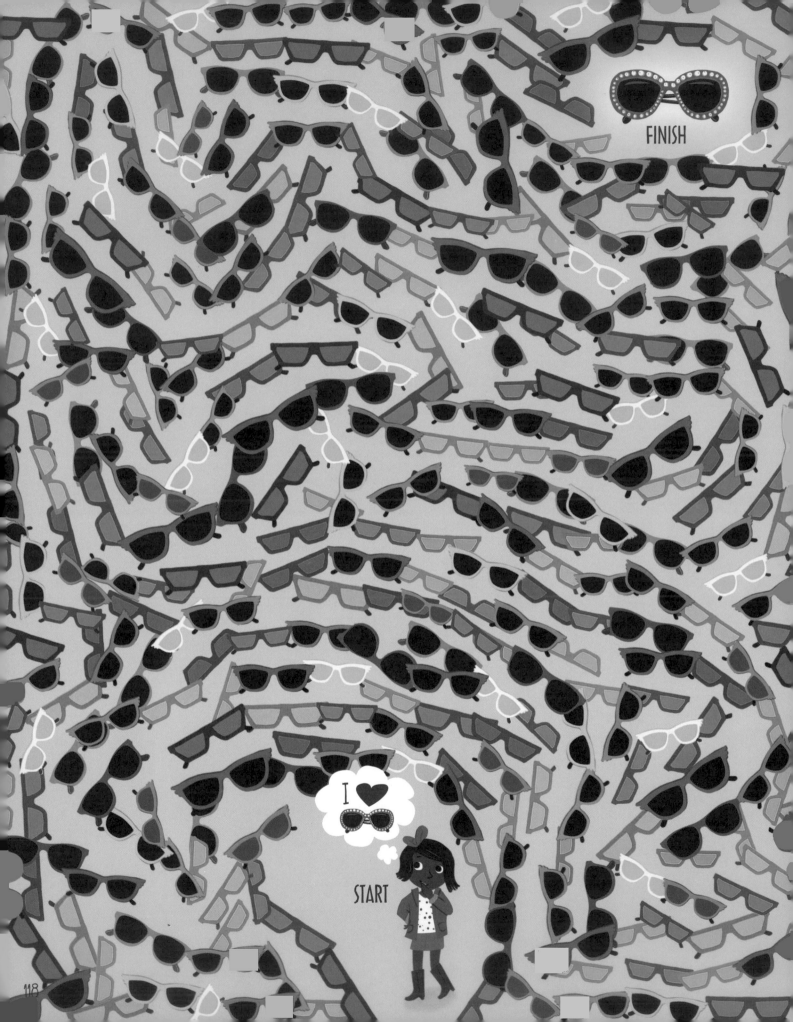

FINISH

I ♥ 👓

START

118

FINISH

121

SOLUTIONS

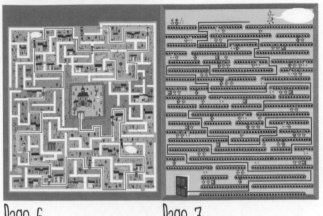

Page 6

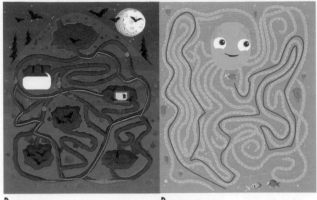

Page 7

Page 8

Page 9

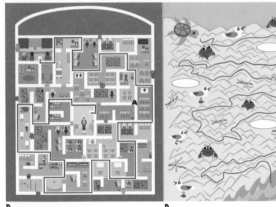

Page 10

Page 11

Pages 12-13

Page 14

Page 15

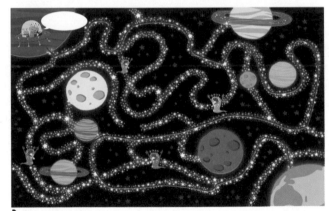

Pages 16-17

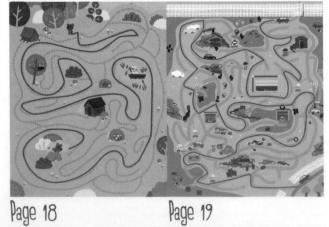

Page 18

Page 19

Pages 20-21

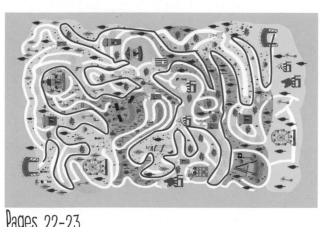

Pages 22-23

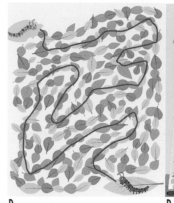

Page 24

Page 25

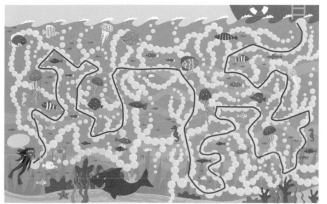

Pages 26-27

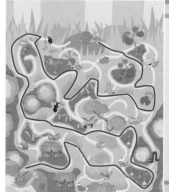

Page 28

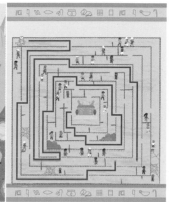

Page 29

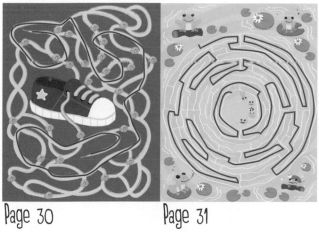

Page 30

Page 31

Pages 32-33

Page 34

Page 35

Page 36

Page 37

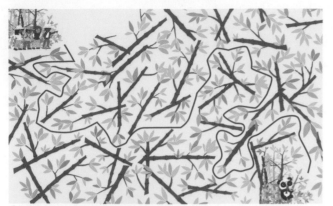

Pages 38-39

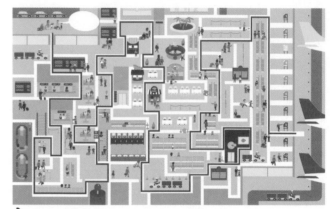

Page 40 Page 41

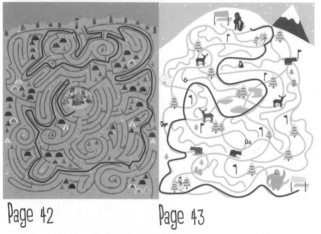

Page 42 Page 43

Pages 44-45

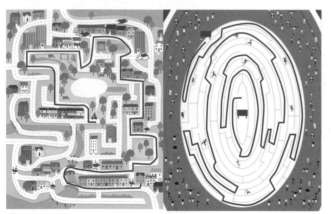

Page 46 Page 47

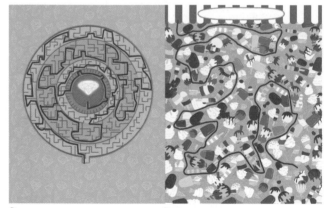

Page 48 Page 49

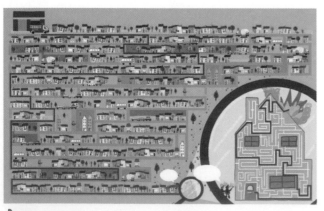

Pages 50-51

Page 52 Page 53

124

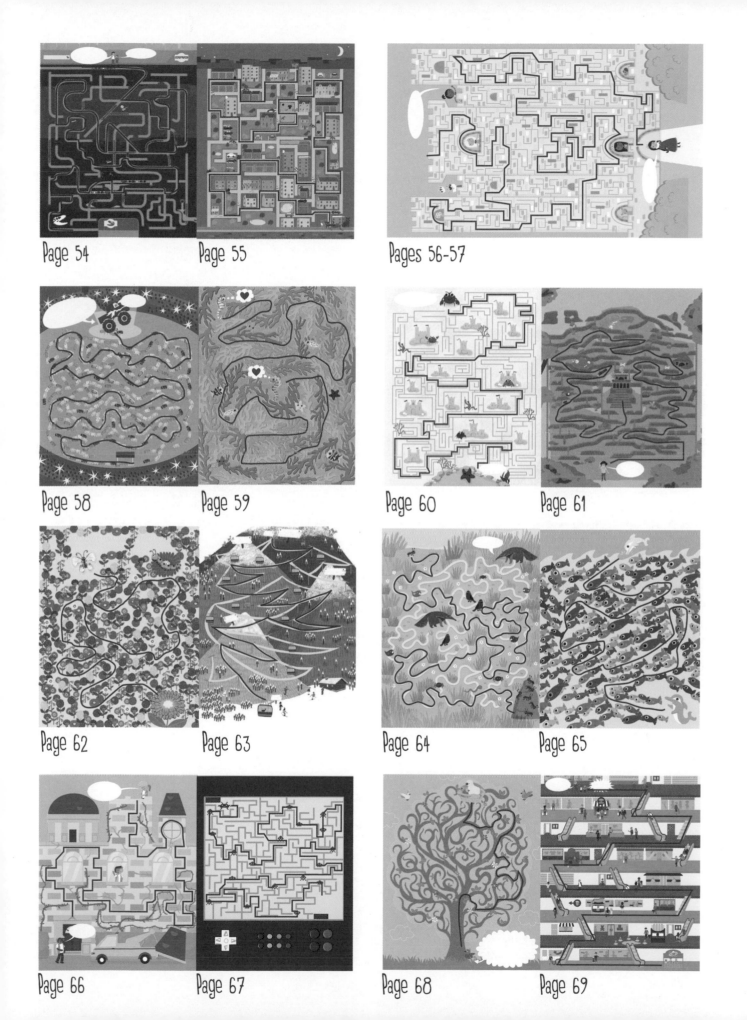

Page 54

Page 55

Pages 56-57

Page 58

Page 59

Page 60

Page 61

Page 62

Page 63

Page 64

Page 65

Page 66

Page 67

Page 68

Page 69

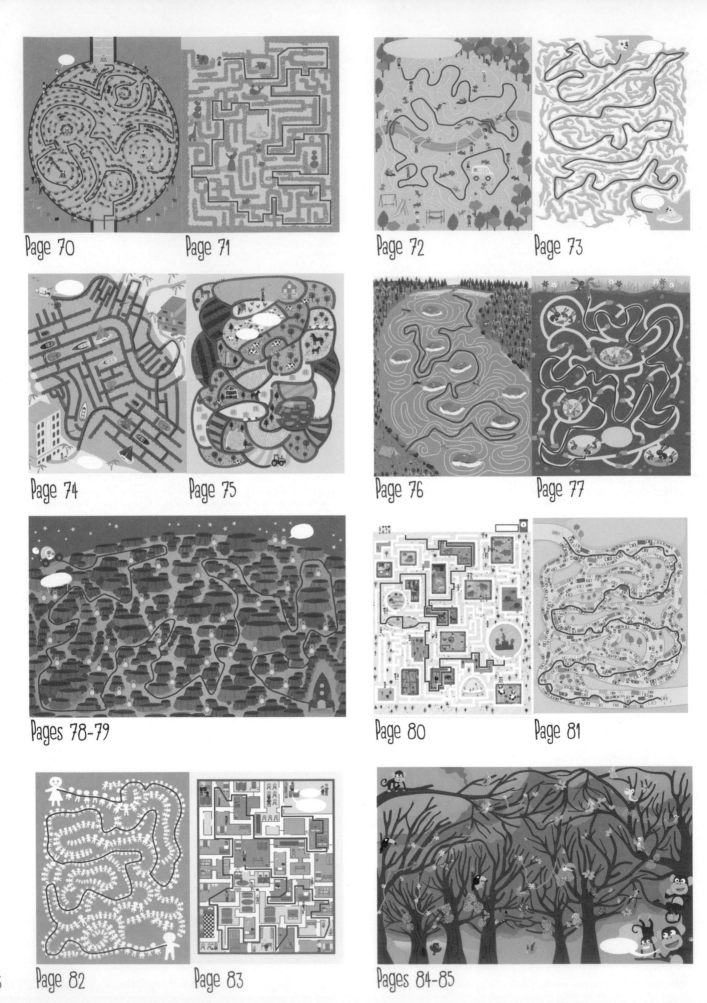

Page 70

Page 71

Page 72

Page 73

Page 74

Page 75

Page 76

Page 77

Pages 78-79

Page 80

Page 81

Page 82

Page 83

Pages 84-85

126

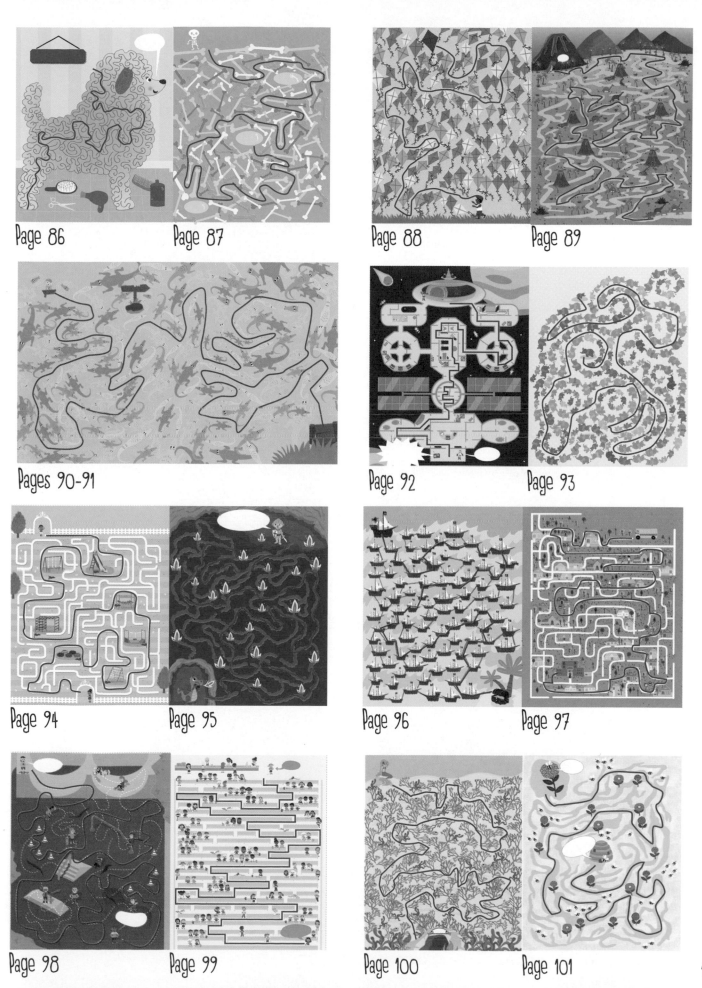

Page 86

Page 87

Page 88

Page 89

Pages 90-91

Page 92

Page 93

Page 94

Page 95

Page 96

Page 97

Page 98

Page 99

Page 100

Page 101

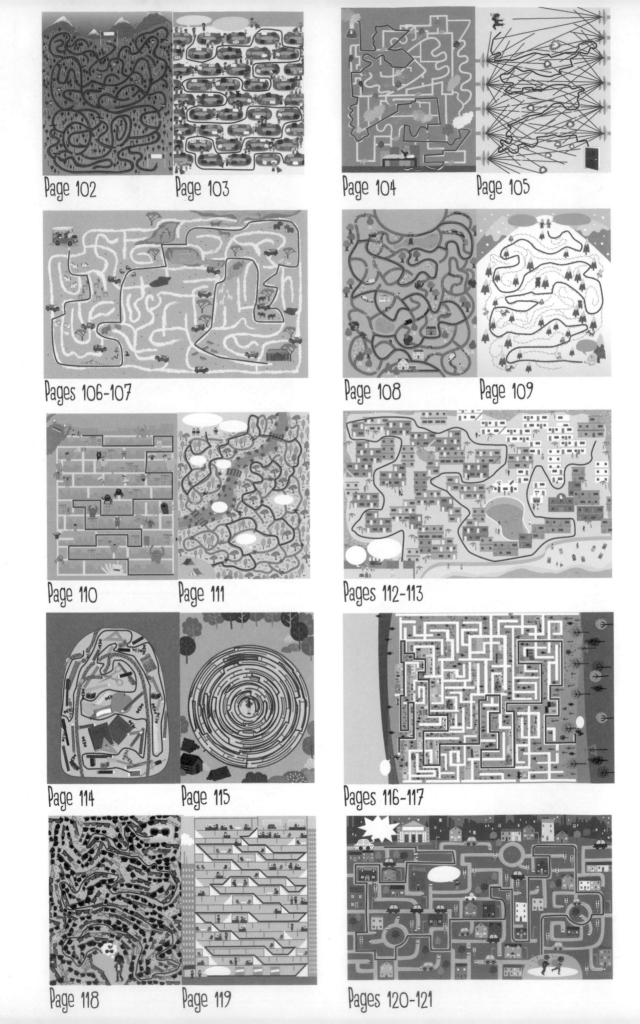

Page 102

Page 103

Page 104

Page 105

Pages 106-107

Page 108

Page 109

Page 110

Page 111

Pages 112-113

Page 114

Page 115

Pages 116-117

Page 118

Page 119

Pages 120-121